Key Facts

The City

The City is where the Chayos are based. The Helix will have to be careful there.

The Chayos

The Chayos are robots that have taken over Earth. They want to find the Helix. Will the Helix defeat them?

Guardians

Noah and Harmony are the guardians of the Helix.

The Story...

The Helix are on the run from the Chayos, robots who have taken over the Earth. The Helix are trying to find their guardians, Harmony and Noah, but will they be able to work out who their friends are?

Mato changes into a bear and pulls Shak to safety.

At the Tainted's base, Shak and Mato look around.
It's locked!
Perhaps I should turn into a snake...

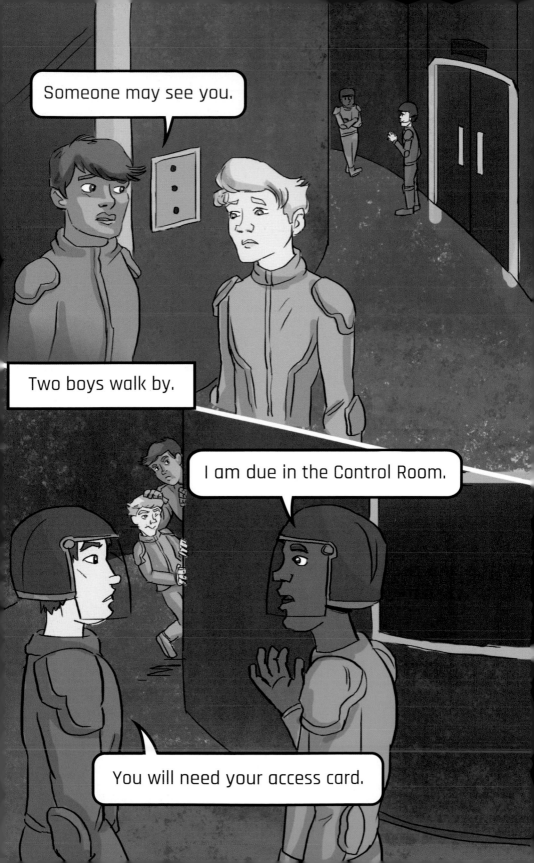

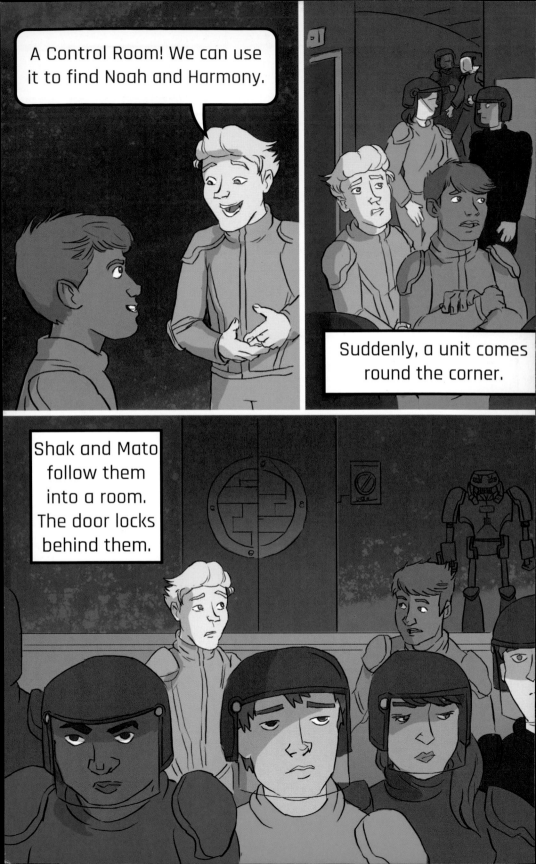

Level Up...

Answer the questions below. Each correct answer gains you points. Are you a Trainee or a Grand Master?

1 *Multiple Choice:*
How do the Helix escape the Chayos? **1pt**
a) They run away
b) They trick them
c) They hide

2 *Multiple Choice:*
Who do Shak and Mato go with?
a) The Chayos **1pt**
b) Harmony and Noah
c) The Tainted

3 Who does Kes meet in the City? **2pts**

4 *Fill in the sentence:*
You will need your _____ card. **3pts**

5 What is happening in the image below? **2pts**

6 *Multiple Choice:*
In the end, where are Shak and Mato locked into? **1pt**
a) A cell
b) A room with the Tainted
c) A ship

Answers on the next page. Every correct answer earns points (pts) Which level are you?

Level:
0 - 1pts = Trainee
2 - 4pts = Novice
5 - 7pts = Adept
8 - 9pts = Expert
10pts = Grand Master

Explore...

Think about what happens next.

- Do you think Kes and Abe will find Shak and Mato in time?

- What might happen if the Mind Sweep works? Do you think Mato and Shak will join the Tainted?

- What would the characters be feeling?

Other Titles

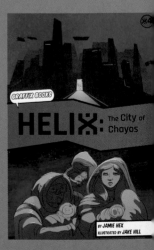